From the movie

Disney FROZEN

ANNUAL 2015

EGMONT

We bring stories to life

First published in Great Britain in 2014 by Egmont UK Limited,
1 Nicholas Road, London, W11 4AN

Written by Catherine Such. Designed by Jeanette Ryall.

© 2014 Disney Enterprises, Inc.

ISBN 978 1 4052 7555 2
58842/4
Printed in Italy

Adult supervision is recommended when glue, paint, scissors and other sharp points are in use.

Stay safe online. Any website addresses listed in this book are correct at the time of going to print. However, Egmont is not responsible for content hosted by third parties. Please be aware that online content can be subject to change and websites can contain content that is unsuitable for children. We advise that all children are supervised when using the internet.

This Frozen annual
belongs to

From the movie

Disney FROZEN

All this inside ...

Frozen Friends

Read on to find out more about the residents of Arendelle and their magical, wintry world.

Princess Anna

Eager to love and be loved, Anna wants nothing more than to once again be close with her older sister, Elsa. There is a lot of tension between the sisters as they grow up - and apart. But Anna's adventurous spirit, persistence, and big heart may be the key to saving her kingdom and her family from an eternal winter, even with a few awkward moments along the way.

Queen Elsa

The first-born child in the royal family of Arendelle, Elsa has kept a secret: she has the magical ability to create ice and snow, and when her emotions rise, her powers are triggered. When Elsa's powers are revealed at her coronation as queen, and all of Arendelle has become frozen in ice, Elsa flees to a mountain to be left alone. There she finally feels free to stop hiding her magic.

Kristoff

A rugged life in the mountains definitely suits this strong, kind, and loyal ice harvester. And it's a good thing he's tough, because the sudden winter storm in the middle of summer will put a big dent in his ice-selling business. His loyal reindeer, Sven, is always by his side. And Kristoff has some mysterious friends up in the mountains.

Olaf

Good-natured and good-humoured, Olaf sees everything from the bright, sunny side. Elsa created him with her magical powers and he lives up in the cold and snowy mountain. He's always dreamed of experiencing summer - but he's never actually done it. This cool guy loves a warm hug!

Sven

Sven is Kristoff's loyal and devoted companion. He and Kristoff have been a team since they were both very young. Ready and willing to help anyone who may be in danger, Sven would think nothing of swimming through an ice-cold fjord to save a friend.

Hans

A handsome and charming royal, Hans meets Princess Anna when he visits Arendelle. He's a younger sibling (of 13 brothers) too, so he and Anna have lots in common. It seems to be love at first sight. After asking Anna to marry him, Hans tries to keep everyone calm when Elsa's powers are revealed.

Marshmallow

This icy snowman's main goal is to protect Elsa and her ice palace. If you make him angry his spikes come out and you'll be sorry! Elsa created him and Olaf named him.

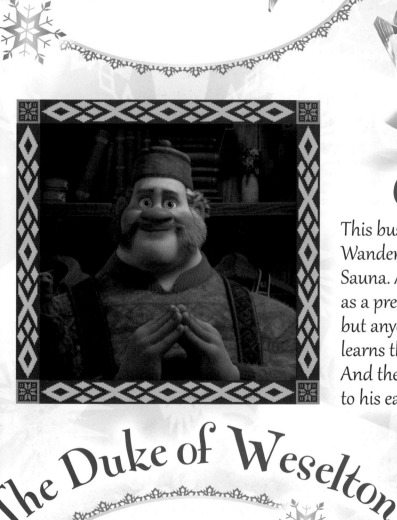

Oaken

This business-minded fellow owns Wandering Oaken's Trading Post and Sauna. At first, Oaken comes across as a pretty easy-going and simple guy, but anyone who messes with him soon learns that he *really* means business. And then he immediately returns to his easy-going self!

The Duke of Weselton

A trading partner with Arendelle, the Duke (shown here with his guards) has been wondering why the kingdom was shut down. Now that the gates will open for Elsa's coronation he plans to make some good money from trading - and maybe enjoy some parties, as well!

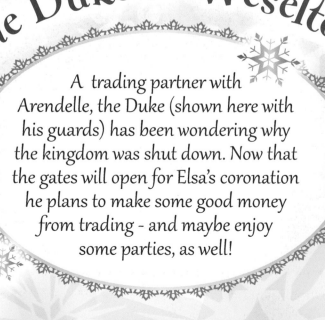

Cool Colouring

Your Frozen friends want to say hello! Use your favourite pens to colour this happy picture.

DISNEY FROZEN

1

In a kingdom long ago and far away, there were two little princesses who were the best of friends. Anna and Elsa loved to play together - especially because Elsa had a magical power. She could create snow and ice, even in the middle of summer!

2

But one night, when the girls were playing together, Anna was accidentally hurt by an icy blast from Elsa. The king and queen were worried that people in the kingdom would not understand Elsa's special powers, so they asked Elsa to hide her magic and they closed the gates to the kingdom.

3

Elsa desperately tried to control her power, but she couldn't help letting it slip out when she got upset. To keep her sister safe, Elsa decided not to play with Anna anymore. Anna didn't understand why Elsa was shutting her out, and she missed her sister terribly.

4

Years passed and the two sisters hardly knew each other. When Elsa turned 21, she was crowned Queen of Arendelle.

5

Anna missed her sister's affection so she was thrilled when, on the day of her sister's coronation, she met a handsome prince named Hans. He showed Anna the kindness and affection she missed so much.

6

Anna and Hans decided to get engaged right away, but Elsa didn't think it was a good idea. "I can't live behind closed gates anymore," exclaimed Anna. "Hans is not just any boy, he's ..." "Enough!" cried Elsa - and as she waved her hand, an icy blast accidentally shot out.

Everyone at the coronation stared in shock. Elsa was terrified that her secret had been revealed - and she was afraid of hurting someone by mistake. She raced out of the castle. Everything froze behind her as she ran through the kingdom.

8 Elsa headed up the North Mountain. She created snow and ice sculptures along the way, as she experimented with her powers. At the top of the mountain she created a magnificent ice palace. Here, she could let go of all her powers without hurting anyone. She finally felt free!

9 But down in Arendelle, everyone was panicking. Elsa's powers had covered Arendelle with snow and ice in the middle of July! So Anna travelled up the mountain to find Elsa. After her horse threw her into the snow, she was lucky to find shelter from the cold.

10 Inside a barn, Anna met Kristoff and his reindeer, Sven. Kristoff knew the mountains well, and he agreed to help Anna find Elsa.

11 Kristoff, Anna and Sven began their journey up the mountain. But soon they came to a deep gorge that was difficult to cross. Behind them, a pack of wolves were closing in! Working together, Anna, Kristoff and Sven finally made it safely across the gorge.

2

As they got closer to the top of the mountain, Anna marvelled at the beautiful winter wonderland her sister had created. The ice sparkled and the snow covered everything like a fluffy blanket. But as Anna looked down at Arendelle, she could see it was getting colder and colder. The people there were in danger!

3

Anna and her new friends were surprised to meet a funny little snowman ... who was alive! His name was Olaf and he was excited to hear about Anna's plans to bring back summer.

14

Olaf had never been in summer weather. He imagined himself basking in the sunshine. But Olaf didn't realise that a snowman like him would simply melt in the hot sun!

15

Olaf guided Anna and Kristoff to the magnificent ice palace. When Anna met Elsa, she pleaded with her sister to come home. Anna told Elsa that Arendelle was freezing and she had to thaw the kingdom out.

16 But Elsa didn't want to return to the kingdom because she was afraid of hurting someone. She worried the villagers would not accept her now. And, she said, she didn't really know how to bring back summer to Arendelle anyway.

17 Anna kept insisting that the sisters could figure it out together. Frustrated, Elsa finally turned and raised her hands. "I can't," she cried. A wave of icy power burst from Elsa's body - and accidentally struck Anna in the chest!

18 Elsa hadn't meant to hurt Anna. She worried she would hurt her again so she ordered Anna and her friends to get out. Then she created a huge snowman to hurry them along.

19 Everyone tumbled to the bottom of the mountain landing safely in the soft snow. But something was wrong. Elsa's icy blast had hit Anna's heart. Now Anna was slowly freezing!

20

Meanwhile, back in Arendelle, Anna's horse had returned without her, so Hans set out to find Anna. But he found Elsa instead, and took her back to Arendelle, where she was put under guard.

21

Up on the mountain, Anna was feeling colder and colder. Kristoff took her to a group of mysterious mountain trolls, who explained to her what had happened. The trolls said an act of true love could thaw a frozen heart.

22

Kristoff was desperate to save Anna so he took Anna back home to the castle so that Hans could break the spell with a kiss.

23

But to Anna's surprise, Hans refused to kiss her. He wanted the kingdom for himself! He never loved her at all! Poor Anna was becoming weaker and soon she would freeze to solid ice.

24 Meanwhile, Elsa struggled to escape from imprisonment in the castle. As she grew more upset and worried, her icy powers spread through the cell and helped her to break free!

25 Out on the fjord, Anna watched in horror as Hans caught up with Elsa and raised his sword against her. Although she was freezing and could barely move, Anna was determined to save her sister.

26 Anna struggled to move forward and threw herself in front of Elsa. And then suddenly she froze to solid ice! Hans brought down his sword on Anna's icy body and the sword shattered to pieces.

27 Elsa spun around and threw her arms around her frozen sister. Then something magical happened. Anna began to thaw out! Anna's act of saving Elsa had broken the spell!

28 Finally understanding that love was the answer to her problems, Elsa was able to bring summer back to Arendelle. That made things difficult for Olaf, though, so Elsa created a permanent little snow cloud to keep him cool. "Ahhhhh," said Olaf, "Much better!"

29 The villagers had witnessed Anna saving Elsa from Hans' deadly sword, so they opened the gates and welcomed the sisters home. Anna and Elsa's joyful reunion made the kingdom a happy place once again. And, of course, Kristoff decided to stay in Arendelle!

THE END

Shadow Shapes

Who doesn't have a shadow?

Can you draw lines to match the colourful shadows below to the correct characters?

a

b

2

3

1

c

d

Answers on page 67.

Amazing Arendelle

The palace gates have opened and Anna is excited to be outside.
Can you spot the close-ups below in the big picture?

Reach Elsa!

Anna, Kristoff, and Sven are trying to get to Elsa's ice palace, but they keep running into obstacles. Help them avoid Marshmallow so they can reach the palace!

2

Start

1

Hint: They need to stop along the way. Make the stops in this order:

1. Go to Oaken's Trading Post for dry clothes.
2. Pick up a snack for Sven.
3. Chat with the trolls.

Finish

Tour the Kingdom

From castles and ice palaces to the rugged mountains, there's so much to discover in this ice-covered land!

Arendelle

The beautiful kingdom of Arendelle is home to Anna, Elsa, and their parents. It is surrounded by water and snowy mountains. When the newly crowned Queen Elsa runs out of her own coronation party, the whole kingdom is frozen over. Only Elsa has the power to bring it back to what it used to be. But will she?

The Church

Elsa's coronation ceremony takes place in this grand cathedral, with many visiting royals in attendance.

The North Mountain

This is where Elsa ends up after running out of her coronation. It may be quite beautiful from afar, but the area is covered in rocks, snow and ice.

The Ice Palace

Elsa realises the range of her powers when she finds that she can build a huge, dazzling ice palace! This beautiful, sparkling - but freezing - structure becomes her new home.

The Castle

Home to Arendelle's royal family, the castle is where we first meet young Princesses Elsa and Anna. In an effort to keep Elsa's abilities a secret, the royal family kept the castle's mighty gates closed for many years.

Snowy Teasers

Wrap up warm and see how quickly you can solve these fun Frozen puzzles!

Pretty Pairs

1

It's snowing again in Arendelle! Draw lines to match these snowflakes into pairs.

a b c d e f g h i j

Snowman Sizes

2

Look closely at these pictures of Olaf. Can you circle the biggest and the smallest?

a b c d

Answers on page 67.

Snowball Fun

3

The friends are having a snowball fight! Can you work out who is hiding behind each of these snowballs?

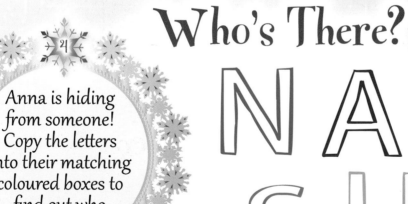

Who's There?

4

Anna is hiding from someone! Copy the letters into their matching coloured boxes to find out who it is.

N A
S H

☐ ☐ ☐ ☐

Who Are You?

Take this quiz to find out which Frozen character you're most like.

1 When friends ask you if you'd like to play a game, you:

   a. Say yes, since you're always ready for some fun!
   b. Only agree to play if you're sure that it's safe.
   c. Say you're not really the game-playing type, but then end up having a great time.
   d. Let someone else answer for you.

2 When you're at a party, you:

   a. Dance!
   b. Have no plans of dancing, no matter what.
   c. Leave. You don't go to parties.
   d. Look around to see where the food is.

3 When you meet someone new, you:

   a. Immediately hope you have lots of things in common. It would be great to make a new friend!
   b. Try not to reveal too much about yourself.
   c. Barely say hello - you have other things to do.
   d. Keep to yourself, especially at first.

4 When you go shopping, you:

   a. Like to be able to choose from a big selection.
   b. Love when gloves are on sale - although you really don't shop much.
   c. Want the prices to be fair.
   d. Wait outside the store, and hope someone brings you a snack.

5 If your town is suddenly covered with ice, you:

a. Have to find a way to fix it.
b. Try to get away so you won't hurt anyone.
c. Think about how this will affect your business.
d. Try not to slip!

6 When you're faced with a huge problem, you:

a. Do your best to come up with a solution.
b. Ignore the problem, and just try to live with it instead.
c. Team up with a loyal friend who will stay with you for as long as it takes.
d. Help your friends fix it, as long as you're not in the middle of a meal.

7 What would you do if you saw a cup with some water in it?

a. Say, "That glass is half full! I love water."
b. Say, "That half-empty glass of water really needs some ice."
c. You might not notice the glass at all!
d. You wouldn't say anything, but you might tip the cup over!

Mostly a

You're positive, outgoing and care about everyone, you and Anna could be twins!

Mostly b

Like Elsa, you are quiet and thoughtful and always look out for your friends.

Mostly c

Just like Kristoff, you work hard and stand up for your friends.

Mostly d

You're loyal and stick with your friends through thick and thin, just like Sven.

Perfect Match

Look closely at these pictures of Elsa and Anna. Can you work out which ones match the originals above?

Elsa Original   Anna Original

a

b

1

2

c

d

3

4

Snow Record

Writer: Alessandro Ferrari; Artist: Iboix Estudi; Colorist: Charles Pickens; Letterer: Patrick Brosseau

Some time ago, inside Arendelle's royal palace ...

Tickle attack!

No! don't tickle me, Anna!

Hahaha...

I can't, Elsa!

Hahahah

FSSSSH

We need to beat the record!

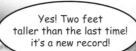

FSSSSH

Hahahahaha

SHROOMMMMMMMMM

Yes! Two feet taller than the last time! it's a new record!

Great... but no more tickling, okay?

The End

33

Icy Hideaway

Elsa loves her magnificent ice palace. Create your own by adding colours and patterns to the frosty picture opposite.

Mirror Message

Anna has left a message for Elsa. Hold this page up to a mirror to reveal what it says.

Do you want to build a snowman?

Elsa has made Anna a sparkling tiara. Give it some icy colours.

Answer on page 67.

Snowy Scene

Olaf, Anna and Kristoff are on their way to the ice palace. How quickly can you answer these questions about the scene?

1

Is Anna's dress blue or green?

2

How many coal buttons does Olaf have?

3

Who is carrying a sack?

4

Does Anna look happy or sad?

Answers on page 67.

Footprints in the Snow

The four friends have left behind trails of footprints in the snow. Draw a line from each group of footprints to the character it belongs to.

Whose image is reflected in the shards of ice?

Kristoff

Sven

Olaf

Anna

a

b

c

d

Answers on page 67.

Sisters Forever

Anna's act of true love in saving her sister melted Anna's frozen heart. Share their happiness and give the sisters some warm colours.

All About Olaf

Let's find out more about Olaf, the loveable snowman who likes warm hugs.

The bright, white snow hurts his eyes!

This is awfully inconvenient for a snowman.

He is noseless until Anna smashes a carrot into his face when they meet.

When Sven approaches Olaf and his new carrot nose, looking for a snack, Olaf thinks the reindeer is trying to give him a kiss!

Sometimes his head is on upside-down.

And sometimes it comes off completely!

He loves the idea of summer - his ultimate dream is to relax in the summer sun!

Let's just let him enjoy that dream!

Sometimes his head falls off.

Snowman Puzzles

Things are always fun when Olaf is about! See how quickly you can finish these exciting activities.

Can you spot all six differences between these two pictures before Olaf melts? Go!

Beach Day

What's Wrong?

Can you figure out the one thing that is wrong with each of these Olafs?

a

b

c

d

Answers on page 67.

How to Scare a Troll

Writer: Alessandro Ferrari. Artist: Iboix Estudi.Colorist: Charles Pickens, Letterer: Patrick Brosseau.

Valley of the trolls. Kristoff has just found his old friends ...

Kristoff! you're back!

Let's play a scary game with Kristoff!

You can't, he's too busy now!

Please! Kristoff's scary games are amazing!

We love them!

I know, kids. but you've got to be patient ...

I can play with you!

?

I know a lot of scary games!

Really?

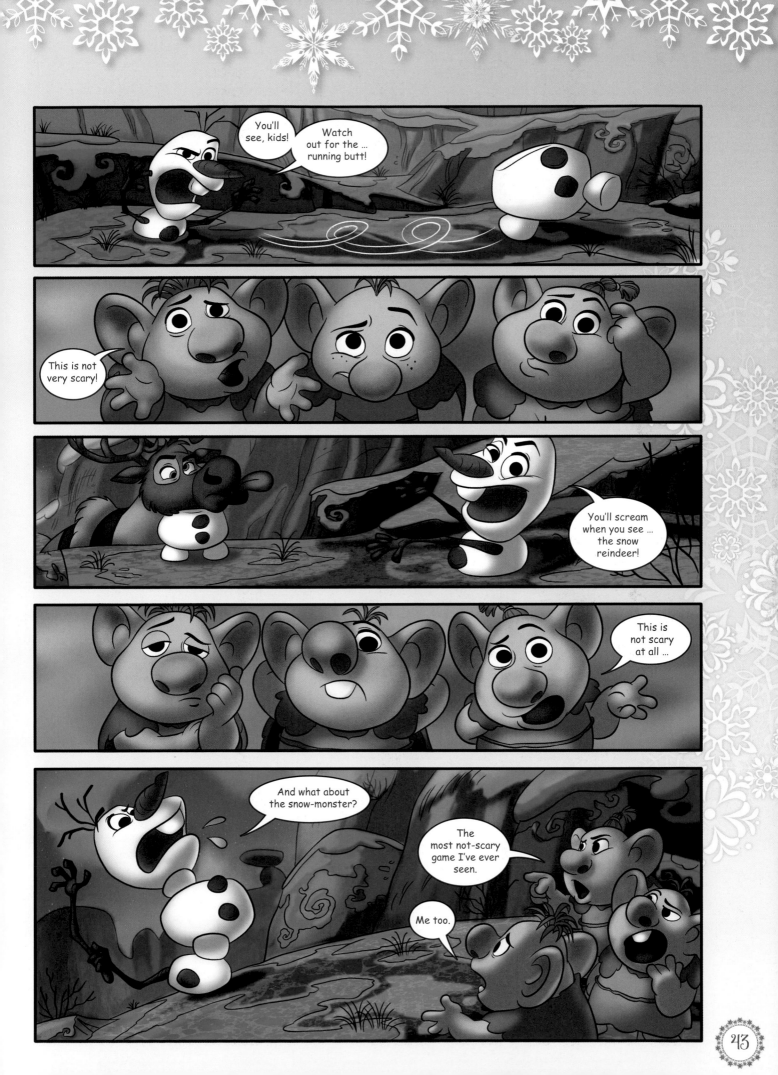

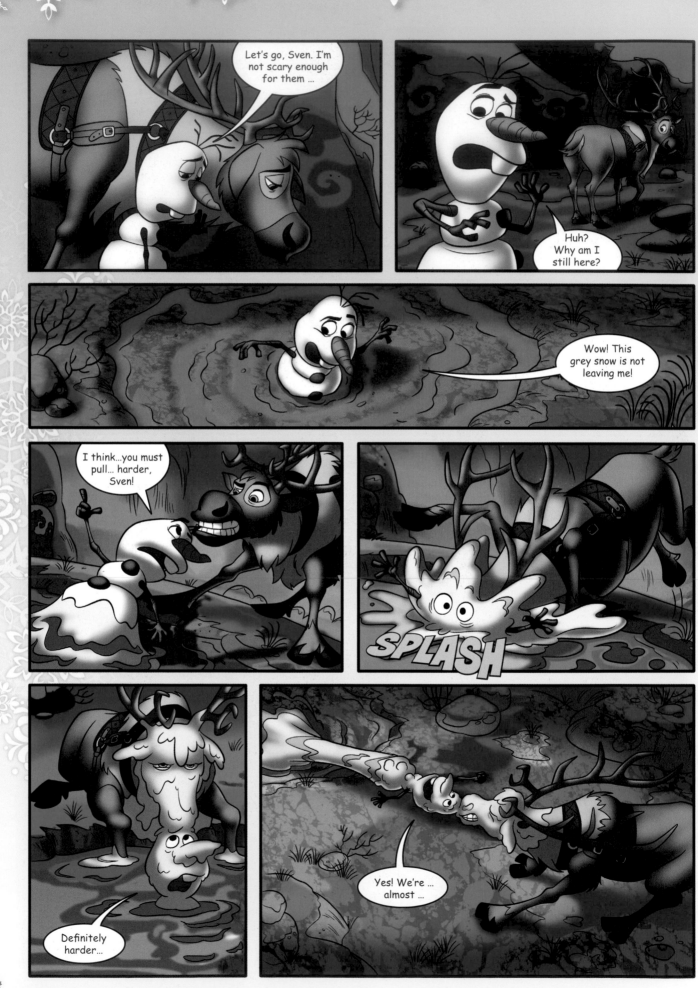

Draw Olaf!

Follow these easy steps to draw your own huggable snowman!

You will Need:

- Paper
- A pencil
- Rubber
- Coloured pencils, paints, markers, or crayons

1 Start with two rough circles for Olaf's body. Add circles for his feet, and a tilted oval for his head. Include two lines to start his arms.

2 Add some detail to his arms, give him a few strands of hair, and draw the top of his mouth and his eyes. (Olaf's eyes are not both the same size.)

3 Draw a small circle in each eye for pupils. Add his nose, eyebrows, and the bottom of his mouth. Draw three circles on his body. (He was waiting for those buttons!) Rub out the lines where your shapes overlap.

4 Add details to Olaf's face: his eyebrows, nose, and mouth. Draw outlines around his arms and hair.

5 Rub out the lines inside his arms and hair. Colour in his pupils with your pencil. Now Olaf is ready for some colour!

Congratulations!
Your drawing of Olaf looks supercool!

Marshmallow Attack!

Match the jigsaw pieces to the spaces to complete this picture of Kristoff and Anna running away from Marshmallow.

1

2

3

4

a

b

c

d

Answers on page 68.

Special Surprise

Kristoff has planned a snow picnic for Anna. Use the colour code to work out where she should meet him.

I P A
C L E

_ _ _

_ _ _ _ _ _

Answer on page 68.

Movie Magic

Let's go behind the scenes of Frozen to discover how buildings, locations and a real-life reindeer helped inspire the movie makers!

Sister Sketches

In the movie, Anna and Elsa's relationship as sisters is very important. However, each girl has a look that's completely her own.

Anna's dresses are long and flowy, with detailed floral patterns.

With snowflakes and sparkles, Elsa's icy gown shimmers like snow.

Model Reindeer

While they were working on the movie, Frozen's animators got to spend some time with a real reindeer, named Sage. They watched Sage carefully so they could make sure Sven's head motions and movements were realistic.

Freeze Frames

In Frozen, Queen Elsa's icy creations are based on real structures that the production team discovered in Quebec, Canada.

Elsa's ice palace has many spires. The artists got their inspiration for the look of her palace from buildings they saw in Quebec.

When they designed the castle in the kingdom of Arendelle, Frozen's production team took ideas and inspiration from the look of this church, in Bergen, Norway.

This ice hotel seating area in Quebec inspired the stunning night-time colours in Frozen - especially the way light shined and reflected through the ice.

Sledge Search

Whoops, Kristoff has lost his sledge in the snow!
Which path does he need to take to find it?

a
b
c

Kristoff

Olaf

Sven

Sledge

Answer on page 68.

Princess Puzzles

Join Anna and Elsa at the Palace to help complete these royal activities.

Party Invitations

Cross out the letters that appear twice to reveal who Elsa has invited to the palace ball.

S C O P L C

D A S F P D

_ _ _ _ _

Odd One Out

Look closely at these pictures of Sven. Can you spot the odd one out?

a

b

c

Answers on page 68.

Jumping for Joy

Use your brightest pens to colour
this happy picture of Anna.

Perfect Palace

Use your magical powers to construct a palace as dazzling as Elsa's. And this one won't melt!

You will Need:
- White paper
- Scissors
- Tape
- Glue
- Glitter
- Hole punch
- Cotton wool
- Plastic wrap

1 Fold a sheet of paper into quarters. Cut all four corners off.

2 Cut shapes out of each edge - squares, triangles, or whatever you want! If you have a hole punch, use it!

3 Unfold the paper so it's flat again.

4 Roll the sheet of paper into a tube shape so the ends are even. Use tape to hold it together. This is the body of your first tower. Take a new sheet of paper and roll it into the shape of a cone for the tower roof. Use tape to hold it together.

5 Use glue to stick glitter onto the roof or cut shapes out of it as decoration.

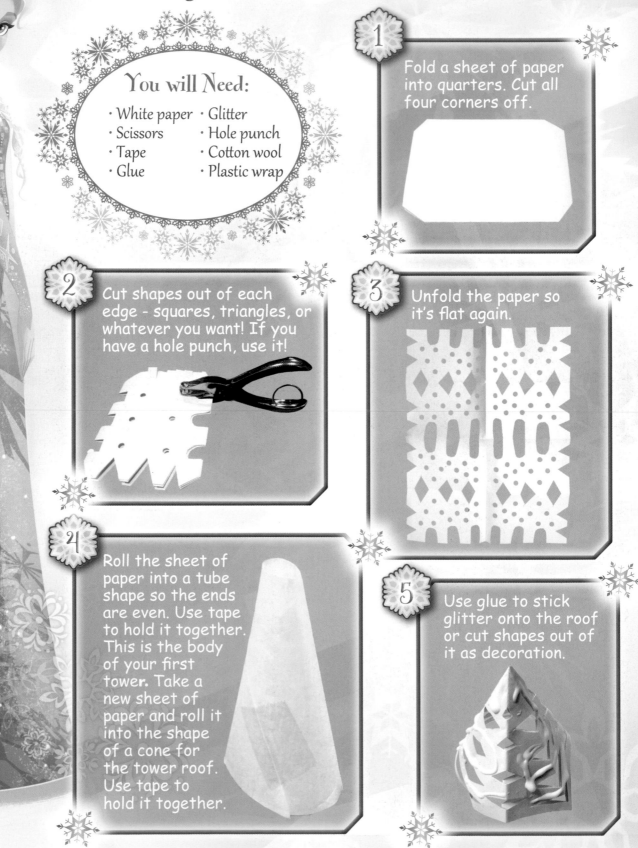

6 Stand the tower on one end and decorate it. Place the roof on top of the tower. Make as many towers as you'd like and set them up together to make a palace!

Here are some palaces you can try yourself:

Tips

- Add clear tape to the bottom edge of each tower to make it stronger.
- Put plastic wrap underneath or around your palace — now you have ice!
- Use cotton wool or hole punches as snow on the ground outside your palace or on the roof!
- Use markers, crayons, coloured pencils, glitter, and paint to decorate your palace.
- Fold and bend sheets of paper to create new shapes (like triangles or arches).

57

Sven to the Rescue

Help Sven find Olaf, then guide them back to Kristoff's sledge.

Start

Finish

1

How many yellow snowflakes has Elsa created?

6 7

A Sunny Snowman

Olaf is dreaming of summer sunshine. Can you spot five differences in the picture at the bottom?

1

Colour in a snowflake each time you spot a difference.

2

Olaf can take himself apart and put himself back together again. How many pieces is he in here?

7 8

Answers on page 68.

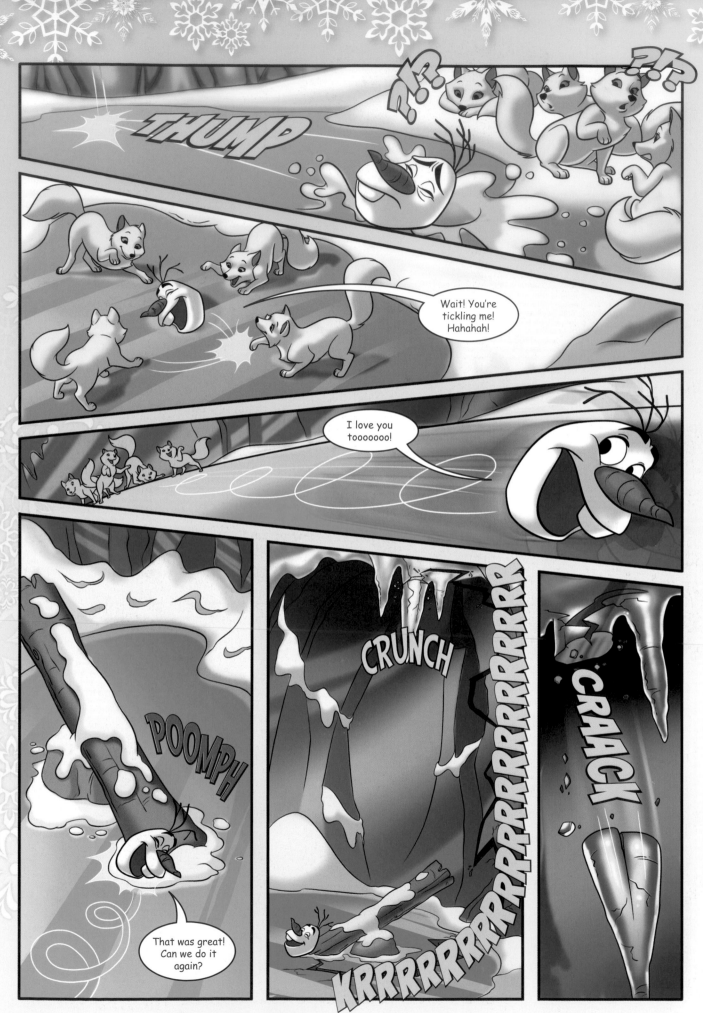

Cool Questions

Find out how well you know your Frozen friends by choosing the correct pictures to answer the questions below.

1

Who pulls Kristoff's sledge?

a   b   c

2

Which picture shows Olaf dreaming of summer?

a   b   c

3

Who made the ice palace?

a   b   c

Add some colour to the pretty snowflakes on the page.

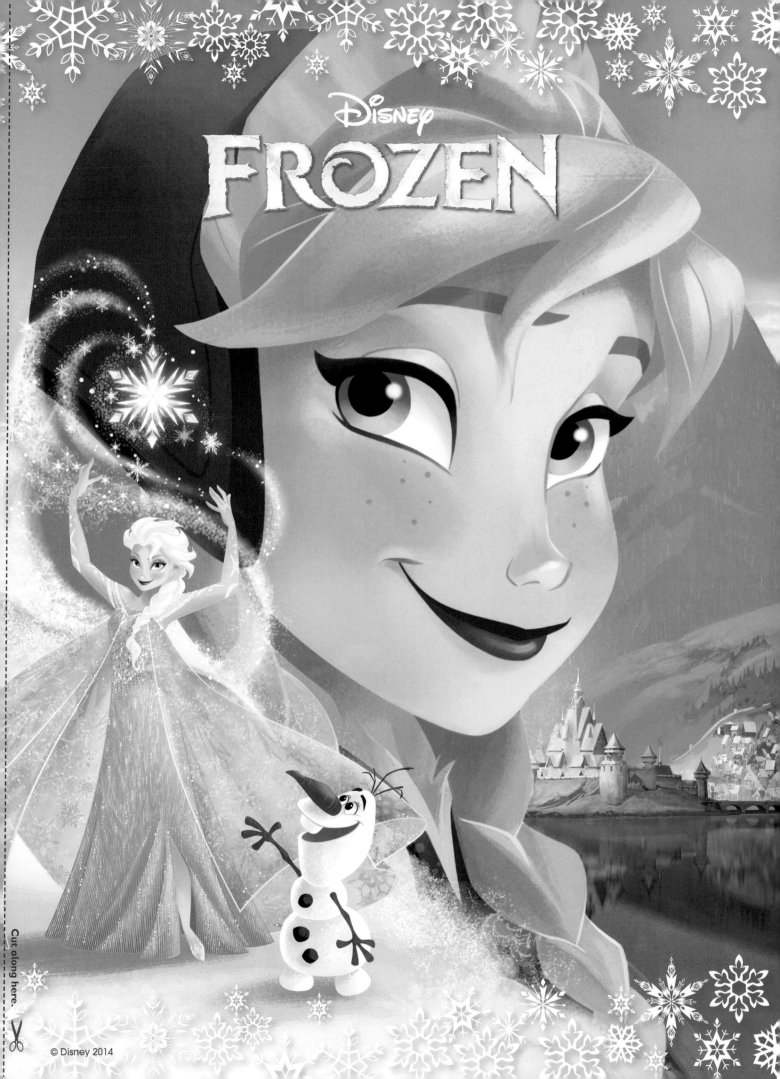

Answers

Page 22
Shadow Shapes
1 – d, 2 – c, 3 – a.
Sven doesn't have a shadow.

Pages 24-25
Reach Elsa!

Pages 28-29
Snowy Teasers

Pretty Pairs: a and i, b and d, c and j, f and h.

Snowman Sizes: Biggest – d, smallest – c.

Snowball Fun: Elsa, Anna and Kristoff.

Who's There?: HANS.

Page 32
Perfect Match
Elsa – a. Anna – 1.

Page 36
Mirror Message
Do you want to build a snowman?

Page 37
Snowy Scene
1. Blue. 2. Three. 3. Kristoff.
4. Happy

Page 38
Footprints in the Snow
a – Sven, b – Anna, c – Olaf, d – Kristoff.
Anna's image is reflected in the shards of glass.

Page 41
Snowman Puzzles
Beach Day:

What's Wrong?:

Answers

Page 48
Marshmallow Attack!
1 – a, 2 – d, 3 – b, 4 – c.

Page 49
Special Surprise
Ice palace.

Page 52
Sledge Search
Path b.

Pages 54-55
Princess Puzzles
Party Invitation: Olaf.
Odd One Out: b.

Page 58
Sven to the Rescue

There are 7 yellow snowflakes.

Page 59
A Sunny Snowman

Olaf is in 7 pieces.

Page 64
Cool Questions
1 – c, 2 – b, 3 – b.

Have you seen Tinker Bell magazine?

Available at all good newsagents and supermarkets.

Out monthly!